PRENTICE HALL MATHEMATICS

ALGEBRA 2

Chapter 11 Support File

Sequences and Series

Prentice Hall

Needham, Massachusetts
Upper Saddle River, New Jersey
Glenview, Illinois

ISBN: 0-13-063820-X

1 2 3 4 5 6 7 8 9 10   06 05 04 03 02

Chapter 11

Sequences and Series

Practice 11-1

Mathematical Patterns

Write a recursive formula for each sequence. Then find the next term.

1. $-14, -8, -2, 4, 10, \ldots$

2. $6, 5.7, 5.4, 5.1, 4.8, \ldots$

3. $1, -2, 4, -8, 16, \ldots$

4. $1, 3, 9, 27, \ldots$

5. $1, \frac{1}{2}, \frac{1}{4}, \frac{1}{8}, \frac{1}{16}, \ldots$

6. $\frac{2}{3}, 1, 1\frac{1}{3}, 1\frac{2}{3}, 2, \ldots$

7. $36, 39, 42, 45, 48, \ldots$

8. $36, 30, 24, 18, 12, \ldots$

9. $9.6, 4.8, 2.4, 1.2, 0.6, \ldots$

Write an explicit formula for each sequence. Then find a_{20}.

10. $7, 14, 21, 28, 35, \ldots$

11. $2, 8, 14, 20, 26, \ldots$

12. $5, 6, 7, 8, 9, \ldots$

13. $-1, 0, 1, 2, 3, \ldots$

14. $3, 5, 7, 9, 11, \ldots$

15. $0.8, 1.6, 2.4, 3.2, 4, \ldots$

16. $\frac{1}{4}, \frac{1}{2}, \frac{3}{4}, 1, \frac{5}{4}, \ldots$

17. $\frac{1}{2}, \frac{1}{4}, \frac{1}{6}, \frac{1}{8}, \frac{1}{10}, \ldots$

18. $\frac{2}{3}, 1\frac{2}{3}, 2\frac{2}{3}, 3\frac{2}{3}, 4\frac{2}{3}, \ldots$

Describe each pattern formed. Find the next three terms.

19. $1, 2, 4, 8, 16, \ldots$

20. $44, 39, 34, 29, 24, \ldots$

21. $0.7, 0.8, 0.9, 1.0, 1.1, \ldots$

22. $4, 11, 18, 25, 32, \ldots$

23. $1\frac{1}{4}, 2\frac{1}{2}, 5, 10, 20, \ldots$

24. $-6, -9, -12, -15, -18, \ldots$

Decide whether each formula is *explicit* or *recursive*. Then find the first five terms of each sequence.

25. $a_n = \frac{1}{3}n$

26. $a_n = n^2 - 6$

27. $a_1 = 5, a_n = 3a_{n-1} - 7$

28. $a_n = \frac{1}{2}(n - 1)$

29. $a_1 = 5, a_n = 3 - a_{n-1}$

30. $a_1 = -4, a_n = 2a_{n-1}$

31. The first figure of a fractal contains one segment. For each successive figure, six segments replace each segment.

   a. How many segments are in each of the first four figures of the sequence?

   b. Write a recursive formula for the sequence.

32. The sum of the measures of the exterior angles of any polygon is 360. All the angles have the same measure in a regular polygon.

   a. Find the measure of one exterior angle in a regular hexagon (six angles).

   b. Write an explicit formula for the measure of one exterior angle in a regular polygon with n angles.

   c. Why would this formula not be meaningful for $n = 1$ or $n = 2$?

Practice 11-2

Arithmetic Sequences

Find the 43rd term of each sequence.

1. $12, 14, 16, 18, \ldots$

2. $13.1, 3.1, -6.9, -16.9, \ldots$

3. $19.5, 19.9, 20.3, 20.7, \ldots$

4. $27, 24, 21, 18, \ldots$

5. $2, 13, 24, 35, \ldots$

6. $21, 15, 9, 3, \ldots$

7. $1.3, 1.4, 1.5, 1.6, \ldots$

8. $-2.1, -2.3, -2.5, -2.7, \ldots$

9. $45, 48, 51, 54, \ldots$

Is the given sequence arithmetic? If so, identify the common difference.

10. $2, 3, 5, 8, \ldots$

11. $0, -3, -6, -9, \ldots$

12. $0.9, 0.5, 0.1, -0.3, \ldots$

13. $3, 8, 13, 18, \ldots$

14. $14, -15, -44, -73, \ldots$

15. $3.2, 3.5, 3.8, 4.1, \ldots$

16. $-34, -28, -22, -16, \ldots$

17. $2.3, 2.5, 2.7, 2.9, \ldots$

18. $127, 140, 153, 166, \ldots$

Find the missing term of each arithmetic sequence.

19. $\ldots 23, \blacksquare, 49, \ldots$

20. $14, \blacksquare, 28, \ldots$

21. $\ldots 29, \blacksquare, 33, \ldots$

22. $\ldots 14, \blacksquare, 15, \ldots$

23. $\ldots -45, \blacksquare, -39, \ldots$

24. $\ldots -5, \blacksquare, -2, \ldots$

25. $-2, \blacksquare, 2, \ldots$

26. $\ldots -6, \blacksquare, 2, \ldots$

27. $-34, \blacksquare, 77, \ldots$

28. $\ldots -45, \blacksquare, -12, \ldots$

29. $-2, \blacksquare, 456, \ldots$

30. $\ldots 34, \blacksquare, 345, \ldots$

Find the arithmetic mean a_n of the given terms.

31. $a_{n-1} - 2, a_{n+1} - 7$

32. $a_{n-1} = 13.2, a_{n+1} = 15.8$

33. $a_{n-1} = 29, a_{n+1} = -11$

34. $a_{n-1} = \frac{2}{5}, a_{n+1} = \frac{4}{5}$

35. $a_{n-1} = 15, a_{n+1} = -17$

36. $a_{n-1} = -6, a_{n+1} = -7$

37. Each year, a volunteer organization expects to add 5 more people to the number of shut-ins for whom the group provides home maintenance services. This year, the organization provides the service for 32 people.

  a. Write a recursive formula for the number of people the organization expects to serve each year.

  b. Write the first five terms of the sequence.

  c. Write an explicit formula for the number of people the organization expects to serve each year.

  d. How many people would the organization expect to serve in the 20th year?

Practice 11-3

Geometric Sequences

Find the missing term of each geometric sequence.

1. 4, ■ , 16, . . .   **2.** 9, ■ , 16, . . .   **3.** 2, ■ , 8, . . .

4. 3, ■ , 12, . . .   **5.** 2, ■ , 50, . . .   **6.** 4, ■ , 5.76, . . .

Is the given sequence geometric? If so, identify the common ratio and find the next two terms.

7. 3, 9, 27, 81, . . .   **8.** 4, 8, 16, 32, . . .   **9.** 4, 8, 12, 16, . . .

10. 4, −8, 16, −32, . . .   **11.** 1, 0.5, 0.25, 0.125, . . .   **12.** 100, 30, 9, 2.7, . . .

13. −5, 0, 5, 10, . . .   **14.** 64, −32, 16, −8, . . .   **15.** 1, 4, 9, 16, . . .

Identify each sequence as _arithmetic, geometric,_ or _neither._ Then find the next two terms.

16. $9, 3, 1, \frac{1}{3}, \ldots$ **17.** 1, 0, −2, −5, . . .   **18.** 2, −2, 2, −2, . . .

19. −3, 2, 7, 12, . . .   **20.** 1, −2, −5, −8, . . .   **21.** 1, −2, 3, −4, . . .

Write the explicit formula for each sequence. Then generate the first five terms.

22. $a_1 = 3, r = -2$ **23.** $a_1 = 5, r = 3$ **24.** $a_1 = -1, r = 4$

25. $a_1 = -2, r = -3$ **26.** $a_1 = 32, r = -0.5$ **27.** $a_1 = 2187, r = \frac{1}{3}$

28. $a_1 = 9, r = 2$ **29.** $a_1 = -4, r = 4$ **30.** $a_1 = 0.1, r = -2$

31. When a pendulum swings freely, the length of its arc decreases geometrically. Find each missing arc length.

   a. 20th arc is 20 in.; 22nd arc is 18.5 in.

   b. 8th arc is 27 mm; 10th arc is 3 mm

32. The deer population in an area is increasing. This year, the population was 1.025 times last year's population of 2537.

   a. Assuming that the population increases at the same rate for the next few years, write an explicit formula for the sequence.

   b. Find the expected deer population for the fourth year of the sequence.

33. You enlarge a picture to 150% of its size several times. After the first increase, the picture is 1 in. wide.

   a. Write an explicit formula to model the size after each increase.

   b. How wide is the photo after the 2nd increase?

   c. How wide is the photo after the 3rd increase?

   d. How wide is the photo after the 12th increase?

Name_____ Class_____ Date_____

Practice 11-4

For each sum, find the number of terms, the first term, and the last term. Then evaluate the series.

1. $\sum_{n=1}^{4} (n-1)$ **2.** $\sum_{n=2}^{6} (2n-1)$ **3.** $\sum_{n=3}^{8} (n+25)$

4. $\sum_{n=2}^{5} (5n+3)$ **5.** $\sum_{n=1}^{4} (2n+0.5)$ **6.** $\sum_{n=1}^{6} (3-n)$

7. $\sum_{n=5}^{10} n$ **8.** $\sum_{n=1}^{4} (-n-3)$ **9.** $\sum_{n=3}^{6} (3n+2)$

Write the related series for each finite sequence. Then evaluate each series.

10. $1, 3, 5, \ldots, 15$ **11.** $5, 8, 11, \ldots, 26$ **12.** $4, 9, 14, 19, \ldots, 44$

13. $10, 25, 40, 55, 70, 85$ **14.** $17, 25, 33, 41, 49, 57, 65$ **15.** $125, 126, 127, \ldots, 131$

Use summation notation to write each arithmetic series for the specified number of terms.

16. $1 + 3 + 5 + \ldots; n = 7$ **17.** $2.3 + 2.6 + 2.9 + \ldots; n = 5$ **18.** $4 + 8 + 12 + \ldots; n = 4$

19. $10 + 7 + 4 + \ldots; n = 6$ **20.** $3 + 7 + 11 + \ldots; n = 8$ **21.** $15 + 25 + 35 + \ldots; n = 7$

Tell whether each list is a *series* or a *sequence*. Then tell whether it is *finite* or *infinite*.

22. $7, 12, 17, 22, 27$ **23.** $3 + 5 + 7 + 9 + \ldots$ **24.** $8, 8.2, 8.4, 8.6, 8.8, 9.0, \ldots$

25. $1 + 5 + 9 + 13 + 17$ **26.** $40, 20, 10, 5, 2.5, 1.25, \ldots$ **27.** $10 + 20 + 30 + 40 + 50$

Each sequence has six terms. Evaluate each related series.

28. $1, 0, -1, \ldots, -4$ **29.** $4, 5, 6, \ldots, 9$ **30.** $-7, -9, -11, \ldots, -17$

31. $-6, -7, -8, \ldots, -11$ **32.** $0, 0.3, 0.6, \ldots, 1.5$ **33.** $5, 7, 9, \ldots, 15$

34. An embroidery pattern calls for 5 stitches in the first row and for three more stitches in each successive row. The 25th row, which is the last row, has 77 stitches. Find the total number of stitches in the pattern.

35. A marching band formation consists of 6 rows. The first row has 9 musicians, the second has 11, the third has 13 and so on. How many musicians are in the last row and how many musicians are there in all?

Practice 11-5

Decide whether each infinite geometric series *diverges* or *converges*. State whether each series has a sum.

1. $3 + \frac{3}{2} + \frac{3}{4} + \ldots$

2. $4 + 2 + 1 + \ldots$

3. $17 + 15.3 + 13.77 + \ldots$

4. $6 + 11.4 + 21.66 + \ldots$

5. $-20 - 8 - 3.2 - \ldots$

6. $50 + 70 + 98 + \ldots$

Evaluate each infinite series that has a sum.

7. $\sum_{n=1}^{\infty} 5\left(\frac{2}{3}\right)^{n-1}$

8. $\sum_{n=1}^{\infty} (-2.1)^{n-1}$

9. $\sum_{n=1}^{\infty} \left(-\frac{1}{2}\right)^{n-1}$

10. $\sum_{n=1}^{\infty} 2\left(\frac{5}{3}\right)^{n-1}$

Evaluate each infinite geometric series.

11. $8 + 4 + 2 + 1 + \ldots$

12. $1 + \frac{1}{3} + \frac{1}{9} + \frac{1}{27} + \ldots$

13. $120 + 96 + 76.8 + 61.44 + \ldots$

14. $1000 + 750 + 562.5 + 421.875 + \ldots$

Determine whether each series is *arithmetic* or *geometric*. Then evaluate the series to the given term.

15. $2 + 5 + 8 + 11 + \ldots; S_9$

16. $\frac{1}{8} + \frac{1}{16} + \frac{1}{32} + \frac{1}{64} + \ldots; S_8$

17. $-3 + 6 - 12 + 24 - \ldots; S_{10}$

18. $-2 + 2 + 6 + 10 + \ldots; S_{12}$

Evaluate the series to the given term.

19. $40 + 20 + 10 + \ldots; S_{10}$

20. $4 + 12 + 36 + \ldots; S_{15}$

21. $15 + 12 + 9.6 + \ldots; S_{40}$

22. $27 + 9 + 3 + \ldots; S_{100}$

23. $0.2 + 0.02 + 0.002 + \ldots; S_8$

24. $100 + 200 + 400 + \ldots; S_6$

25. This month, Julia deposits $400 to save for a vacation. She plans to deposit 10% more each successive month for the next 11 months. How much will she have saved after the 12 deposits?

26. Suppose your business made a profit of $5500 the first year. If the profit increases 20% per year, find the total profit over the first 5 yr.

27. The end of a pendulum travels 50 cm on its first swing. Each swing after the first travels 99% as far as the preceding one. How far will the pendulum travel before it stops?

28. A seashell has chambers that are each 0.82 times the length of the next chamber. The outer chamber is 32 mm around. Find the total length of the shell's spiraled chambers.

29. The first year a toy manufacturer introduces a new toy, its sales total $495,000. The company expects its sales to drop 10% each succeeding year. Find the total expected sales in the first 6 yr. Find the total expected sales if the company offers the toy for sale for as long as anyone buys it.

Practice 11-6

Write and evaluate a sum to approximate the area under each curve for the domain $0 \leq x \leq 2$.

   a. Use inscribed rectangles 0.5 unit wide.

   b. Use circumscribed rectangles 0.5 unit wide.

1. $y = -x^2 + 4$ **2.** $f(x) = -2x^2 + 16$ **3.** $g(x) = -0.5x^2 + 2$

4. $f(x) = x^2 + 4$ **5.** $y = 2x^2 + 6$ **6.** $h(g) = 0.5x^2 + 2$

7. $y = -3x^2 + 15$ **8.** $f(x) = 3x^2 + 2$ **9.** $f(x) = 10 - x^2$

10. a. Graph the curve $y = 2x^2 + 1$.

     b. Use inscribed rectangles to approximate the area under the curve for the interval $0 \leq x \leq 2$ and rectangle width of 0.5 unit.

     c. Repeat part b using circumscribed rectangles.

     d. Find the mean of the areas you found in parts b and c. Of the three estimates, which best approximates the area for the interval?

Use your graphing calculator to find the area under each curve for the domain $-2 \leq x \leq 1$.

11. $y = -x^3 + 1$ **12.** $f(x) = -2x^3 + 3$ **13.** $f(x) = 2x^2 + 1$

14. $g(x) = 3x^2 + 1$ **15.** $y = -\frac{1}{4}x^2 + 1$ **16.** $f(x) = 4x^2 + 2$

17. $y = -x^2 + 4$ **18.** $f(x) = x^2 + 1$ **19.** $y = \sqrt{x + 3}$

Given each set of axes, what does the area under the curve represent?

20. y-axis: feet per second, x-axis: seconds

21. y-axis: computers produced per day, x-axis: days

22. y-axis: miles per hour, x-axis: hours

23. y-axis: gallons per minute, x-axis: minutes

24. y-axis: molecules per second, x-axis: seconds

25. y-axis: price per pound of apples, x-axis: pounds of apples

Graph each curve. Use inscribed rectangles to approximate the area under the curve for the interval and rectangle width given.

26. $y = \frac{1}{4}x^2, 2 \leq x \leq 4, 1$ **27.** $y = x^3 + 1, 0 \leq x \leq 2, 0.5$

Reteaching 11-1

Mathematical Patterns

OBJECTIVE: Finding the nth term in a sequence	**MATERIALS:** None

Some patterns are much easier to determine than others. Here are some tips that can help with unfamiliar patterns.

- If the terms become progressively smaller, subtraction or division may be involved.

- If the terms become progressively larger, addition or multiplication may be involved.

Example

Find the next term in this sequence: 6, 8, 11, 15, 20, . . .

     6   8   11   15   20   ⟵   **Spread the numbers in the sequence apart, leaving space between numbers.**

       +2   +3   +4   +5   ⟵   **Beneath each space, write what can be done to get the next number in the sequence.**

In each term, the number that is added   ⟵   **Find a pattern.**
to the previous term increases by one.

If the pattern is continued, the next term is 20 + 6, or 26.

Exercises

Describe the pattern that is formed. Find the next three terms.

1. 38, 33, 28, 23, . . .   **2.** 7, 14, 28, 56, . . .   **3.** −5, −7, −9, −11, . . .

4. 2, 6, 18, 54, . . .   **5.** 4.5, 5, 5.5, 6, . . .   **6.** 17, 19, 23, 29, . . .

Match each sequence on the left with a statement on the right.

7. 9, 15, 21, 27, . . .   **A.** The next term in the sequence is −2.

8. 9, 10.5, 13.5, 19.5, . . .   **B.** The sixth term is 39.

9. 3, 2.5, 1.5, 0, . . .   **C.** Each term is one half of the previous term.

10. −4, 4, 12, 20, . . .   **D.** Each term is two times the previous term.

11. 32, 16, 8, 4, . . .   **E.** The fifth term is 31.5.

12. 2, 4, 8, 16, . . .   **F.** The eighth term is 52.

Reteaching 11-2

OBJECTIVE: Finding the nth term of an arithmetic sequence	**MATERIALS:** None

Example

Find the 15th term of an arithmetic sequence whose first three terms are 20, 16.5, and 13.

$20 - 16.5 = 3.5$
$16.5 - 13 = 3.5$ ⟵   **First, find the common difference. The difference between consecutive terms is 3.5. The sequence decreases. The common difference is −3.5.**

$a_n = a_1 + (n - 1)\, d$ ⟵   **Use the explicit formula.**

$a_{15} = 20 + (15 - 1)(-3.5)$ ⟵   **Substitute $a_1 = 20$, $n = 15$, and $d = -3.5$.**

$= 20 + (14)(-3.5)$ ⟵   **Subtract within parentheses.**

$= 20 + -49$ ⟵   **Multiply.**

$= -29$ ⟵   **The 15th term is −29.**

Check the answer. Write $a_1, a_2, \ldots, a_{15}$ down the left side of your paper. Start with $a_1 = 20$. Subtract 3.5 and record 16.5 next to a_2. Continue until you find a_{15}.

Exercises

Find the 25th term of each sequence.

1. $20, 18, 16, 14, \ldots$ **2.** $0.0057, 0.0060, 0.0063, \ldots$

3. $4, 0, -4, -8, \ldots$ **4.** $0.2, 0.7, 1.2, 1.7, \ldots$

5. $-10, -8.8, -7.6, -6.4, \ldots$ **6.** $22, 26, 30, 34, \ldots$

7. Suppose you begin to work selling ads for a newspaper. You will be paid $50.00/wk plus a minimum of $7.50 for each potential customer you contact. What is the least amount of money you earn after contacting eight businesses in 1 wk?

8. In March, Jaime starts a savings account for a mountain bike. He initially deposits $15.00. He decides to increase each deposit by $8.00. How much is his seventeenth deposit?

9. Sue is knitting a blanket for her infant niece. Each day, she knits four more rows than the day before. She knitted seven rows on Sunday. How many rows did she knit on the following Saturday?

Reteaching 11-3

Geometric Sequences

OBJECTIVE: Finding the nth term of a geometric sequence	**MATERIALS:** None

- A geometric sequence has a constant ratio between consecutive terms. This ratio is the common ratio.

- A geometric sequence formula can be written as a recursive formula, $a_n = a_{n-1} \cdot r$, or as an explicit formula, $a_n = a_1 \cdot r^{n-1}$.

Example

Find the 12th term of the geometric sequence $5, 15, 45, \ldots$.

$5, 15, 45, \ldots$

$r = \dfrac{15}{5} = \dfrac{45}{15} = 3$ ← **Find r by calculating the common ratio between consecutive terms. This is a geometric sequence because there is a common ratio between consecutive terms.**

$a_n = 5(3)^{n-1}$ ← **Substitute $a_1 = 5$ and $r = 3$ into the explicit formula to find a formula for the nth term of the sequence.**

$a_{12} = 5(3)^{11}$ ← **Substitute $n = 12$ to find the 12th term of the sequence.**

$a_{12} = 885{,}735$ ← **Remember to first calculate 3^{11}, then multiply by 5.**

Exercises

Find the indicated term of the geometric sequence.

1. $4, 2, 1, \ldots$ Find a_{10}.

2. $5, \dfrac{15}{2}, \dfrac{45}{4}, \ldots$ Find a_8.

3. $6, -2, \dfrac{2}{3}, \ldots$ Find a_{12}.

4. $1, -\dfrac{2}{3}, \dfrac{4}{9}, \ldots$ Find a_7.

5. $100, 200, 400, \ldots$ Find a_9.

6. $8, 32, 128, \ldots$ Find a_4.

Write the explicit formula for each sequence. Then generate the first five terms.

7. $a_1 = 1, r = \dfrac{1}{2}$

8. $a_1 = 2, r = 3$

9. $a_1 = 12, r = 3$

10. $a_1 = 1, r = \dfrac{1}{4}$

11. $a_1 = 5, r = \dfrac{1}{10}$

12. $a_1 = 1, r = \dfrac{1}{3}$

13. $a_1 = 5, r = 2$

14. $a_1 = 1, r = 3$

15. $a_1 = 3, r = 6$

16. $a_1 = 3, r = 3$

17. $a_1 = 2, r = 2$

18. $a_1 = 2, r = \dfrac{1}{2}$

19. $a_1 = 1, r = \dfrac{1}{5}$

20. $a_1 = 3, r = 4$

21. $a_1 = 5, r = \dfrac{1}{4}$

Reteaching 11-4

OBJECTIVE: Finding the sum of a given number of terms of a series

MATERIALS: None

Example

Evaluate the series $\displaystyle\sum_{n=2}^{4}(5-2n)$.

$$\sum_{n=②}^{④}\boxed{(5-2n)}$$

← Circle the upper and lower limits. Box the explicit formula.

$$(n=2) \qquad (n=3) \qquad (n=4)$$

← In circles, write all possible values of *n*, beginning with the lower limit and ending with the upper limit.

$$(n=2) \qquad (n=3) \qquad (n-4)$$
$$\boxed{5-2(2)} \qquad \boxed{5-2(3)} \qquad \boxed{5-2(4)}$$

← Under each circle, draw a box; copy the explicit formula, substituting the value in the circle above the box for the value of *n*.

$$(n=2) \qquad (n=3) \qquad (n=4)$$
$$\sum_{n=2}^{4}(5-2n) = \boxed{5-2(2)} + \boxed{5-2(3)} + \boxed{5-2(4)}$$

← The value of the series is the sum of the values in the boxes.

$$= \quad 1 \quad + \quad (-1) \quad + \quad (-3)$$

← Evaluate each expression.

$$= \quad -3$$

← Find the sum of the terms.

The sum of the series is -3.

Exercises

Evaluate each series.

1. $\displaystyle\sum_{n=1}^{3}(n-4)$

2. $\displaystyle\sum_{n=1}^{4}\frac{1}{3n}$

3. $\displaystyle\sum_{n=3}^{8}(3n-1)$

4. $\displaystyle\sum_{n=3}^{8}\frac{2n}{3}$

5. $\displaystyle\sum_{n=3}^{9}(4-2n)$

6. $\displaystyle\sum_{n=1}^{5}8n$

7. $\displaystyle\sum_{n=2}^{7}4n$

8. $\displaystyle\sum_{n=1}^{7}(3-2n)$

9. $\displaystyle\sum_{n=2}^{5}(5n+1)$

10. An outdoor amphitheater has 45 rows of seats. The first row has 89 seats. The last row has 177 seats. Each row has 2 more seats than the previous row. Write an explicit formula representing the number of seats in the *n*th row. Then find the sum of the 45 rows of seats.

Reteaching 11-5

Geometric Series

OBJECTIVE: Finding the sum of a finite and of an infinite geometric series

MATERIALS: None

- The sum of a finite geometric series is the sum of the terms of a geometric sequence. This sum can be found by using the formula $S_n = \frac{a_1(1 - r^n)}{1 - r}$, where a_1 is the first term, r is the common ratio, and n is the number of terms.

- The sum of an infinite geometric series with $|r| < 1$ is found by using the formula $S = \frac{a_1}{1 - r}$, where a_1 is the first term and r is the common ratio. If $|r| \geq 1$, then the series has no sum.

Example

Find the sum of the first ten terms of the series
$8 + 16 + 32 + 64 + 128 + \ldots$

$a_1 = 8$ ←   **a_1 is the first term in the series.**

$r = \frac{16}{8} = \frac{32}{16} = \frac{64}{32} = \frac{128}{64} = 2$ ←   **Simplify the ratio formed by any two consecutive terms to find r.**

$n = 10$ ←   **n is the number of terms in the series to be added together.**

$S_{10} = \frac{8(1 - 2^{10})}{1 - 2}$ ←   **Substitute $a_1 = 8$, $r = 2$, and $n = 10$ into the formula for the sum of a finite geometric series.**

$= \frac{8(-1023)}{-1}$ ←   **Simplify inside the parentheses.**

$= 8184$ ←   **Simplify.**

Exercises

Evaluate the series to the given term.

1. $3 + 12 + 48 + 192 + \ldots; S_6$

2. $8 + 2 + \frac{1}{2} + \frac{1}{8} + \ldots; S_5$

3. $-10 - 5 - 2.5 - 1.25 - \ldots; S_7$

4. $10 + (-5) + \frac{5}{2} + \left(-\frac{5}{4}\right) + \ldots; S_{11}$

Evaluate each infinite geometric series.

5. $10 + 5 + 2.5 + \ldots$

6. $-1 + \frac{2}{11} - \frac{4}{121} + \ldots$

7. $\frac{1}{4} + \frac{7}{32} + \frac{49}{256} + \ldots$

8. $\frac{1}{2} - \frac{1}{5} + \frac{2}{25} - \ldots$

9. $-\frac{1}{6} + \frac{1}{12} - \frac{1}{24} + \ldots$

10. $20 + 16 + \frac{64}{5} + \ldots$

11. $12 + 4 + \frac{4}{3} + \ldots$

12. $\frac{1}{4} - \frac{1}{8} + \frac{1}{16} - \ldots$

13. $\frac{2}{3} + \frac{2}{15} + \frac{2}{75} + \ldots$

Reteaching 11-6

OBJECTIVE: Developing area under a curve as a series	**MATERIALS:** Graph paper, colored pencils

You can use rectangles to approximate the area under the curve $f(x)$. You can use summation notation to represent the sum of the areas of these rectangles.

$$A = \sum_{n=1}^{b} (w)f(a_n)$$

← number of rectangles

↑ width of each rectangle   ↑ function value at a_n

Example

Graph $f(x) = x^2 + 2$. Use inscribed rectangles 0.5 units wide to approximate the area under the curve for $0 \le x \le 2$.

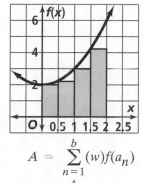

← **Draw the curve on the grid.**

← **Determine and label the interval endpoints. Counting from 0 to 2 by 0.5 units, we get 4 intervals with endpoints at 0, 0.5, 1, 1.5, and 2.**

← **Draw segments from these endpoints on the x-axis to the graph of f. When using inscribed rectangles, the shortest of each consecutive pair of segments represents the height of the rectangle. Draw and shade these 4 rectangles.**

$A = \sum_{n=1}^{b} (w)f(a_n)$ ← **Write the formula.**

$= \sum_{n=1}^{4} (0.5)f(a_n)$ ← **Substitute $b = 4$ since there are 4 rectangles, and $w = 0.5$ since each rectangle is 0.5 units wide.**

$= (0.5)f(a_1) + (0.5)f(a_2) + (0.5)f(a_3) + (0.5)f(a_4)$ ← **Expand the summation.**

$= (0.5)(2) \quad + (0.5)(2.25) + (0.5)(3) \quad + (0.5)(4.25)$ ← **$f(a_1)$ is the height of the first rectangle. This corresponds to $f(0)$ which is 2. Similarly determine the heights of the remaining rectangles: $f(0.5) = 2.25$, $f(1) = 3$, and $f(1.5) = 4.25$.**

$= 0.5(2 + 2.25 + 3 + 4.25)$ ← **Use the Distributive Property.**

$= 5.75$ ← **Simplify.**

The area is approximately 5.75 units^2.

Exercises

Use the method shown in the Example to approximate the area under each curve for the interval $0 < x \le 2$. Use inscribed rectangles 0.5 unit wide.

1. $f(x) = 2x^2$

2. $f(x) = -x^2 + 4$

3. $y = 2x + 3$

4. $y = -x + 2$

5. $f(x) = x^2 + 1$

6. $f(x) = -x^2 + 6$

Enrichment 11-1

Meaningful Relationships

For each of the following sequences, use the given recursive formula to compute the value of the indicated term. Then write the letter associated with the sequence on the dash whose number corresponds with the value of the term you have found.

<u>___</u> <u>___</u> <u>___</u> <u>___</u> <u>___</u> <u>___</u> <u>___</u> <u>___</u> <u>___</u> <u>___</u> <u>___</u> <u>___</u> <u>___</u> <u>___</u> <u>___</u> <u>___</u> <u>___</u>
1   2   3   4   5   6   7   8   9   10   11   12   13   14   15   16   17

Letter	a_1	a_{n+1}	Find:
A	-2	$a_n + 2$	a_5
A	3	$2a_n$	a_3
E	1	2^{a_n}	a_4
G	0	$2a_n + 2$	a_4
I	-5	$a_n + 4$	a_5
I	2	$\frac{1}{a_n}$	a_7
I	0	$3a_n + 1$	a_3
L	5	$a_n + 5$	a_3
L	9	$-a_n + (-1)^{n+1}$	a_5
M	81	$(a_n)^{1/2}$	a_3
N	-4	$a_n + 1$	a_{18}
R	4	$a_n + 2^{n-1}$	a_3
R	10^{10}	$\log a_n$	a_2
S	1	$-a_n$	a_7
S	45	$a_n - 4$	a_8
T	3	$(a_n - 1)^2$	a_3

Enrichment 11-2

One Fish, Two Fish?

Complete the grid below to find the names of three underwater inhabitants.

	C1	C2	C3	C4	C5	C6	C7	C8	C9	C10
R1										
R2										
R3										
R4										
R5										
R6										

Two terms of an arithmetic sequence are given. Use those two terms to determine a_1 and d for the sequence. Then use the value of a_1 to determine a row number, and use the value of d to determine a column number from the table below. Now write the letter associated with the sequence in the square of the above grid that corresponds to the row and column numbers you have determined. What underwater inhabitants appear in the grid?

a_1	Row	d	Column
-3	R1	-4	C1
-2	R2	-3	C2
-1	R3	-2	C3
0	R4	-1	C4
1	R5	0	C5
2	R6	1	C6
		2	C7
		3	C8
		4	C9
		5	C10

Letter	Sequence terms		Letter	Sequence terms
A	$a_3 = -3, a_8 = -8$		N	$a_3 = -3, a_6 = -9$
A	$a_3 = 0, a_6 = -3$		N	$a_4 = 14, a_8 = 30$
A	$a_3 = 6, a_7 = 22$		O	$a_3 = 9, a_5 = 17$
E	$a_2 = 2, a_9 = 9$		S	$a_2 = 1, a_6 = 17$
H	$a_4 = -8, a_6 = -12$		T	$a_5 = -17, a_7 = -25$
L	$a_5 = 0, a_7 = 0$		U	$a_3 = -6, a_9 = -24$
L	$a_3 = 7, a_5 = 15$		W	$a_5 = -15, a_7 = -21$
M	$a_3 = 8, a_7 = 24$			

Enrichment 11-3

• •

Doubling Periods in Geometric Sequences

Consider the geometric sequence $3, 4\frac{1}{2}, 6\frac{3}{4}, 10\frac{1}{8}, \ldots$.

1. How are the terms of the sequence related?

2. For any term of the sequence, how many terms does it take before the value of the term has at least doubled?

   The doubling period of a geometric sequence is the number of terms needed to reach a term at least twice as large as a given term. What is the doubling period for the given sequence?

3. Write the first ten terms of the geometric sequence $a_1 = 3, r = 1.1$ to two decimal places.

4. What is the doubling period for $a_1 = 3$? for $a_2 = 3.3$?

   Although the doubling period does not depend on which term is given, it does depend on the common ratio. For what value(s) of r is the doubling period of a geometric sequence greater than 1?

The idea of a *doubling period* applies to certain everyday situations. For example, under optimum conditions, bacteria reproduce by splitting in two. Suppose at noon on a certain day, there are 1000 bacteria in a dish. At 6 P.M. on the same day, there are 8000 bacteria.

5. If a count is taken every hour, how many terms are in the geometric sequence? What is the common ratio? What is the doubling period?

6. If a count is taken every 40 minutes, how many terms are in the sequence? What is the common ratio? What is the doubling period?

7. In both cases, how many hours does it take the bacteria to double?

Enrichment 11-4

. . . .

The Gauss Trick

Suppose your teacher asked you to add the numbers from 1 to 100. You
would probably begin by adding $1 + 2 + 3 + \ldots + 100$, term by term from
left to right. Karl Friedrich Gauss (1777–1855) found another way. Let S
represent the finite series whose sum we are trying to find. Since addition is
commutative, both equations below represent this series.

$$S = \quad 1 + 2 + 3 + \ldots + 98 + 99 + 100$$

$$S = 100 + 99 + 98 + \ldots + 3 + 2 + 1$$

1. What is the sum of the quantity on the left side of the first equation and
the quantity on the left side of the second equation?

2. What is the sum of each vertically-aligned pair of quantities on the right
side of the equal signs?

3. How many such pairs are there?

4. Since each pair has the same sum, use multiplication to express the sum
of all the pairs on the right side.

5. Write an equation that states that the sum of the left sides must equal
the sum of the right sides. Solve your equation for *S*.

Use the technique outlined above to derive the formula for the sum of *n*
terms of any arithmetic series. Suppose that the series starts with the term a_1
and has a common difference of *d*.

6. What is the *n*th term?

7. Write the sum *S* of the *n* terms of the series. Then write the sum in
reverse order, lining up terms.

8. What is the sum of each vertical pair of quantities on the right side?

9. How many such pairs are there?

10. Express the sum of all the pairs using multiplication.

11. Write an equation that states that the sum of the left sides must equal
the sum of the right sides. Solve your equation for *S*.

12. Show that your equation is equivalent to $S = \frac{n}{2}(a_1 + a_n)$. Hint: Use
your answer to Exercise 6.

Enrichment 11-5

Sums of Geometric Series

According to legend, the game of chess was invented by a Persian nobleman. The sultan asked the nobleman what he wanted as a reward. The nobleman took out a board that had 64 squares. He asked the sultan to put 1 grain of wheat on the first square, 2 grains on the second, 4 on the third, and so on, doubling the number of grains on each successive square.

1. Complete the table showing the number of grains the nobleman would receive by the time the sultan had reached the sixth square.

Square Number	Number of Grains on that Square, a_n	Total Number of Grains on the Board, S_n
1	1	1
2	2	3
3	4	7
4		
5		
6		

2. What is the first term of the sequence, a_1?

3. Is this sequence arithmetic, geometric, or neither? If applicable, find the common difference or common ratio.

4. Write a recursive formula for a_{n+1}.

5. Write an explicit formula for a_{n+1}.

6. Find a_{15}. What does this number represent?

7. Determine whether the series S_n is arithmetic, geometric, or neither.

8. For the values in the table, compare each value of S_n with a_{n+1}.

9. Use your answer to Exercise 4 to write a recursive formula for S_n.

10. Use your answer to Exercise 5 to write an explicit formula for S_n.

11. Find S_{29}. What does this number represent?

Now imagine a tournament with 2^n contestants in which contestants are paired off.

12. How many matches will be played?

13. How many losers will there be? How many winners?

14. How many new matches will be played if these winners are paired off?

15. How many losers will there be in these matches? How many winners will remain?

Algebra 2 Chapter 11

Enrichment 11-6

Researchers Use Area Under a Curve

Scientists collect data through experiments. Collected data needs to be
analyzed to get information that is meaningful. Hydrologists study flooding
to help predict future flood behavior and determine how to prevent it.
Streams are monitored after storms for the amount of water flowing past
the equipment over time. This is called *discharge* and is measured in liters
per second. Models of the data produce the graph below.

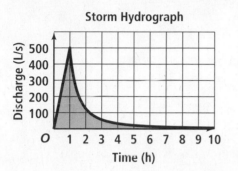

The part of the graph for the domain values $0 \leq x \leq 1$ is represented by
$f(x) = 500x$. The part of the graph for the domain values $1 < x \leq 10$ is
represented by $f(x) = 500x^{-2}$.

The area under the curve gives the volume of water going past the
equipment for the time interval specified. In a storm report, a hydrologist
would need to answer the following questions.

1. What is the total volume of water that passed by in 10 h? (Use
   inscribed rectangles 0.5 unit wide.)

2. During which hour did the greatest volume of water go past the
   equipment? What was the volume of water that passed by during that
   hour? (Use inscribed rectangles 0.5 unit wide.)

3. Access the $\int f(x)dx$ feature from the CALC menu of your graphing
   calculator. What is the total volume of water that passed by in
   10 h? During which hour did the greatest volume of water go past
   the equipment? What was the volume of water that passed by during
   that hour?

4. If the hydrologist recommends measures to keep the rate of discharge
   over the 10 h constant, what would that rate be for the total volume of
   water determined in Exercise 3?

Chapter 11 Project: Get the Picture

Beginning the Chapter Project

When a book such as your mathematics book is being created, artists, designers, and photographers work with writers and editors to make the pages visually attractive. These professionals often work with patterns involving arithmetic and geometric sequences.

In this project, you will see how perspective affects perceived lengths and distances. You will use grids to change the sizes of drawings. You also will learn how a designer crops a photo, then enlarges or reduces it.

List of Materials

- Calculator
- Metric ruler
- Graph paper (variety of grid sizes)

Activities

Activity 1: Researching
Research the concepts of one- and two-point perspective and vanishing points in art.

- Measure the lengths of the arrows shown at the right. What is the relationship between these lengths? How does this relate to your research on perspective?

- Trace the four arrows at the right, moving the paper to the left after tracing the longest arrow so that it is further away from the others than it is now. What do you notice?

- Create a simple drawing of three or more similar objects whose lengths can be represented by an arithmetic sequence. Write the corresponding arithmetic sequence, and a recursive or explicit formula for that sequence.

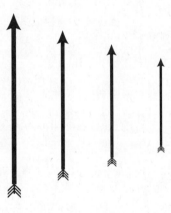

Activity 2: Creating
When a book is made, the text for each page is usually typeset and placed on the page first. Then, any artwork needed for the page is set in place. Often, a designer or artist must change the size of an original sketch to fit the space available on a page. One way to change the dimensions of a sketch is to use graph paper with different size squares.

- Draw a figure or design on a sheet of graph paper. Label this *Figure 1* and record the approximate dimensions of the figure.

- Enlarge the original figure by copying each portion of *Figure 1,* square by square, onto a sheet of graph paper with larger squares. Label this *Figure 2* and record its dimensions.

- Use a ratio to compare the dimensions of *Figure 1* to the dimensions of *Figure 2*. If the same ratio is used to enlarge *Figure 2*, what would the dimensions of the new figure be? Draw this figure, label it *Figure 3,* and record its dimensions. (Note: You may need to create your own grid if graph paper with squares of the appropriate size is not available.)

Figure 1   **Figure 2**

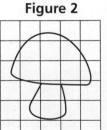

Chapter 11 Project (continued)

- Explain why the lengths of the three figures form a geometric sequence.

- Write a geometric sequence corresponding to these lengths, and a recursive or explicit formula for that sequence.

Activity 3: Analyzing

Photographs are often cropped so that only part of the photograph remains. Then, this cropped portion can be reduced or enlarged. Choose a photograph in a textbook. Place a piece of paper over the photograph, trace its original size, and draw a rectangle to indicate a portion of the photograph that you would like to crop. Draw a diagonal from the lower left corner to the upper right corner of the rectangular cropped area. If this diagonal is extended through the upper right corner of the cropped area, and a point selected anywhere along the diagonal or its extension, then the rectangle having the chosen point as its upper right corner (and the same lower left corner as the original cropped area) will have dimensions that are proportional to the dimensions of the cropped area.

- Measure the dimensions and the length of the diagonal of the cropped area to the nearest centimeter.

- Write the first four terms of an arithmetic sequence that has the length of the diagonal of the cropped area as its first term. Using the terms of your sequence as diagonal lengths, find the four corresponding photo widths. What do you notice about this list of widths?

- Write the first four terms of a geometric sequence that has the length of the diagonal of the cropped area as its first term. Using the terms of your sequence as diagonal lengths, find the four corresponding photo widths. What do you notice about this list of widths?

Finishing the Project

The answers to the activities should help you complete your project. Prepare a presentation or demonstration that summarizes how an artist, a designer, or a photographer uses sequences. Present this information to your classmates. Then discuss the sequences you created.

Reflect and Revise

Review your summary. Are your drawings clear and correct? Are your sequences accurate? Practice your presentation in front of at least two people before presenting it to the class. Ask for their suggestions for improvement.

Extending the Project

Geometric and arithmetic patterns are used in other aspects of design and in other careers. Research other areas where sequences are applied.

Take it to the NET

Visit PHSchool.com for information and links you might find helpful as you complete your project.

Chapter Project Manager
· ·
Chapter 11: Get the Picture

Getting Started
Read the project. As you work on the project, you will need a calculator, a metric ruler, at least two types of graph paper, and materials on which you can record your calculations. Keep all of your work for the project in a folder.

Checklist

☐ Activity 1: relating perspective and arithmetic sequences

☐ Activity 2: relating dimensions and geometric sequences

☐ Activity 3: relating photo-cropping and sequences

☐ presentation

Suggestions

☐ Use art books from the school library or the Internet.

☐ Use grid paper to draw simple geometric designs.

☐ Measure directly or use proportions to find the widths.

☐ Does your display include examples of both arithmetic and geometric sequences? What artists or work of art with which you are familiar best demonstrate the concepts of one-point perspective, two-point perspective, or vanishing points?

Scoring Rubric

3 Calculations, sequences, and formulas are correct. Drawings are neat, accurate, and clearly show the sequences. Explanations are thorough and well thought out.

2 Calculations, sequences, and formulas are mostly correct with some minor errors. Drawings are neat and mostly accurate. Explanations lack detail or are not completely accurate.

1 Calculations contain both minor and major errors. Drawings are not accurate.

0 Major elements of the project are incomplete or missing.

Your Evaluation of Project Evaluate your work, based on the *Scoring Rubric.*

Teacher's Evaluation of Project

Chapter Project Teacher Notes

Chapter 11: Get the Picture

About the Project
The Chapter Project gives students an opportunity to use sequences, explicit formulas, and recursive formulas to change the sizes of drawings and photos. They investigate perspective, the use of grids to enlarge and reduce, and ways to crop, enlarge, and reduce photographs.

Introducing the Project
- Ask students if they have ever seen artists draw buildings or other objects that appear to recede in the distance.

- Ask them why it appears that railroad track rails get closer together when we look at them in the distance.

- Explain that they will investigate the concepts of perspective and vanishing points, and the mathematics involved in enlarging, reducing, and cropping pictures and photographs.

Activity 1: Researching
Students research perspective, create drawings in perspective, write arithmetic sequences, and determine explicit or recursive formulas for their sequences.

Activity 2: Creating
Students use grid paper to enlarge designs. They use the same ratios repeatedly to create lengths which form geometric sequences. They then write explicit or recursive formulas for their sequences.

Activity 3: Analyzing
Students crop photos. Then they enlarge the cropped portions, writing sequences for the widths of enlargements.

Finishing the Project
You may wish to plan a project day on which students share their completed projects. Encourage students to explain their processes as well as their results.

- Have students review their methods for writing explicit and recursive formulas for arithmetic and geometric sequences.

- Ask groups to share their insights that resulted from completing the project, such as any shortcuts they found for creating their drawings or writing formulas.

Take It to the NET

Visit PHSchool.com for information, student links, and teacher support for this project.

✔ Checkpoint Quiz 1

Use with Lessons 11-1 through 11-3.

Identify each sequence as *arithmetic* or *geometric*. Then find the common difference or common ratio.

1. $13, 19, 25, 31, \ldots$

2. $16, 24, 36, 54, \ldots$

3. $4, 14, 24, 34, \ldots$

4. $1, 4, 16, 64, \ldots$

5. $35, 33, 31, 29, \ldots$

6. $64, 48, 36, 27, \ldots$

Find the fifth term of each sequence.

7. $a_1 = 20, a_n = \frac{1}{2}a_{n-1} + 2$

8. $a_n = 8n - 5$

9. $a_1 = \frac{1}{2}, a_n = 2a_{n-1}$

10. Writing Explain how the common ratio for a geometric sequence with positive terms determines whether the terms increase or decrease.

11. In June, you start a holiday savings account with a deposit of $50. You increase each monthly deposit by $2 until the end of the year. Write a recursive formula for the sequence of deposits. How much money will you have saved by December?

- - - - - ✀ -

✔ Checkpoint Quiz 2

Use with Lessons 11-4 through 11-5.

Determine whether each series is *arithmetic* or *geometric*. Then evaluate the series to the given term.

1. $1 + 3 + 9 + \ldots; S_8$

2. $5 + 7 + 9 + \ldots; S_8$

3. $25 + 32 + 39 + \ldots; S_{12}$

4. $256 + 192 + 144 + \ldots; S_7$

5. $1 - 3 + 9 - 27 + \ldots; S_{10}$

6. $-14 + (-7) + 0 + 7 + \ldots; S_{10}$

Evaluate each infinite geometric series.

7. $\sum_{n=1}^{\infty} \left(-\frac{1}{2}\right)^{n-1}$

8. $\sum_{n=1}^{\infty} 3(0.4)^{n-1}$

9. Open-Ended Write an arithmetic series that has a negative sum.

10. Critical Thinking Can an infinite geometric series converge when the common ratio is greater than 1? Explain. Give an example.

Chapter Test

Form A

Chapter 11

Write a recursive and an explicit formula for each sequence. Then find a_{10}.

1. $41, 46, 51, 56, 61, \ldots$ **2.** $1, 10, 100, 1000, 10000, \ldots$ **3.** $3, 6, 12, 24, 48, \ldots$

4. On October 1, a gardener plants 20 bulbs. On October 2, she plants 23 bulbs. On October 3, she plants 26 bulbs. She continues in this pattern until October 15, on which she plants the last bulbs.

   a. Write an explicit formula to model the number of bulbs she plants each day.

   b. Write a recursive formula to model the number of bulbs she plants each day.

   c. How many bulbs will the gardener plant on October 15?

   d. What is the total number of bulbs she plants from October 1 to October 15, inclusive?

Determine whether each sequence is *arithmetic*, *geometric*, or *neither*. Then find the ninth term.

5. $3, 12, 48, 192, \ldots$ **6.** $-2, -7, -12, -17, \ldots$

7. $10, 2, \frac{2}{5}, \frac{2}{25}, \ldots$ **8.** $\frac{1}{2}, 2, \frac{7}{2}, 5, \ldots$

Find the arithmetic mean a_n of the given terms.

9. $a_{n-1} = 8, a_{n+1} = 18$ **10.** $a_{n-1} = -4, a_{n+1} = 8$

11. $a_{n-1} = 0, a_{n+1} = 5$ **12.** $a_{n-1} = \frac{2}{3}, a_{n+1} = 4$

13. Open-Ended Write a sequence and describe it using both an explicit and recursive formula.

Determine whether each sequence is *arithmetic* or *geometric*. Then identify the common difference or the common ratio.

14. $1854, 1788, 1722, 1656, 1590, \ldots$ **15.** $18, 45, 112.5, 281.25, 703.125, \ldots$

16. $1, -4, 16, -64, 256, \ldots$ **17.** $-125, -108, -91, -74, -57, \ldots$

18. $6, 2, \frac{2}{3}, \frac{2}{9}, \ldots$ **19.** $\frac{3}{4}, \frac{13}{12}, \frac{17}{12}, \frac{7}{4}, \ldots$

Generate the first four terms of each sequence; r is a common ratio, and d is a common difference.

20. $a_1 = 3, r = -2$ **21.** $a_1 = 6, d = 4$ **22.** $a_1 = 1000, r = \frac{1}{10}$

23. $a_1 = -4, d = -2$ **24.** $a_1 = \frac{1}{2}, r = -3$ **25.** $a_1 = -100, r = \frac{1}{10}$

Find the missing term of each geometric sequence.

26. $16, \blacksquare, 4$ **27.** $25, \blacksquare, 225$

28. $2, \blacksquare, 50$ **29.** $1, \blacksquare, 49$

30. $\frac{3}{4}, \blacksquare, 3$ **31.** $36, \blacksquare, 4$

Chapter Test (continued)   Form A

Chapter 11

Find the sum of each infinite geometric series.

32. $30 + 22.5 + 16.875 + \ldots$

33. $15 - 3 + 0.6 - 0.12 + \ldots$

34. $12 + 6 + 3 + \ldots$

35. $4 - 2 + 1 - \frac{1}{2} + \ldots$

36. $-13\frac{1}{2} + 9 - 6 + \ldots$

37. $-5 - \frac{5}{2} - \frac{5}{4} - \ldots$

Determine whether each series is *arithmetic* or *geometric*. Then find the sum to the given term.

38. $5 + 9 + 13 + 17 + \ldots; S_{10}$

39. $35 + 70 + 140 + 280 + \ldots; S_7$

40. $6 + (-18) + 54 + (-162) + \ldots; S_8$

41. $8 + 11 + 14 + 17 + \ldots; S_6$

42. $10 + 8 + 6 + 4 + \ldots; S_{10}$

43. $20 + 4 + \frac{4}{5} + \frac{4}{25} + \ldots; S_{10}$

For each sum, find the number of terms, the first term, and the last term. Then evaluate the series.

44. $\sum_{n=1}^{6} (-2n + 5)$

45. $\sum_{n=1}^{5} 4(0.5)^{n-1}$

46. Writing Explain why an infinite geometric series with $r = 1$ diverges. Include an example in your explanation.

47. Suppose you are building 10 steps with 6 concrete blocks in the top step and 60 blocks in the bottom step. If the number of blocks in each step forms an arithmetic sequence, find the total number of concrete blocks needed to build the steps.

Given each set of axes, what does the area under the curve represent?

48. y-axis: feet per second^2; x-axis: seconds

49. y-axis: dollars per pound; x-axis: pounds

50. y-axis: calories per ounce; x-axis: ounces

Graph each curve. Use inscribed rectangles 1 unit wide to approximate the area under the curve for the given interval.

51. $y = -x^2 + 4, -1 \leq x \leq 1$

52. $y = -\frac{1}{2}x + 4, 1 \leq x \leq 5$

Chapter Test

Chapter 11

Form B

Write a recursive and an explicit formula for each sequence. Then find a_{10}.

1. 23, 30, 37, 44, 51, ...

2. $\frac{1}{16}, \frac{1}{4}, 1, 4, 16, ...$

3. 5, 7, 9, 11, 13, ...

4. On December 1, 1 in. of snow falls. On December 2, 1.25 in. of snow falls. On December 3, 1.5 in. of snow falls. The snow continues in this pattern until December 15, after which the snow stops falling.

    a. Write an explicit formula to model the amount of snow that falls each day.

    b. Write a recursive formula to model the amount of snow that falls each day.

    c. How much snow will fall on December 15?

    d. What is the total amount of snow that falls from December 1 to December 15, inclusive?

Determine whether each sequence is *arithmetic, geometric,* or *neither.* Then find the ninth term.

5. 3, 5, 8, 12, 17, ...

6. 1024, 256, 64, 16, 4, ...

7. 8, 4, 2, 1, ...

8. $\frac{3}{2}, \frac{1}{2}, \frac{1}{6}, \frac{1}{18}, ...$

Find the arithmetic mean a_n of the given terms.

9. $a_{n-1} = 26, a_{n+1} = 36$

10. $a_{n-1} = -21, a_{n+1} = -7$

11. $a_{n-1} = \frac{3}{4}, a_{n+1} = \frac{13}{4}$

12. $a_{n-1} = -5, a_{n+1} = -\frac{37}{5}$

13. Writing Explain how to find the geometric mean of two numbers.

Determine whether each sequence is *arithmetic* or *geometric.* Then identify the common difference or the common ratio.

14 36, 90, 225, 562.5, 1406.25, ...

15. 3116, 3062, 3008, 2954, 2900, ...

16. $-448, -416, -384, -352, -320, ...$

17. $1, -6, 36, -216, 1296, ...$

18. $\frac{1}{3}, -\frac{1}{3}, -1, -\frac{5}{3}, ...$

19. $\frac{4}{5}, \frac{1}{5}, \frac{1}{20}, \frac{1}{80}, ...$

Generate the first four terms of each sequence; r is a common ratio, and d is a common difference.

20. $a_1 = 4, r = -2$

21. $a_1 = 22, d = 4$

22. $a_1 = 100, r = \frac{1}{10}$

23. $a_1 = 3, r = -2$

24. $a_1 = \frac{1}{6}, d = 1\frac{1}{2}$

25. $a_1 = -12, r = -\frac{1}{6}$

Find the missing term of each geometric sequence.

26. 500, ■ , 20

27. 12, ■ , 108

28. 20, ■ , 45

29. $\frac{3}{4}$, ■ , 3

30. 48, ■ , $\frac{3}{4}$

31. 1, ■ , 36

Chapter Test (continued)   Form B

Chapter 11

Find the sum of each infinite geometric series.

32. $10 + 1 + \frac{1}{10} + \frac{1}{100} + \ldots$ **33.** $9 - 3 + 1 - \frac{1}{3} + \ldots$

34. $15 + 5 + \frac{5}{3} + \ldots$ **35.** $6 - 3 + \frac{3}{2} - \frac{3}{4} + \ldots$

36. $\frac{8}{3} + \frac{4}{3} + \frac{2}{3} + \frac{1}{3} + \ldots$ **37.** $-16 - 4 - 1 - \frac{1}{4} - \ldots$

Determine whether each series is *arithmetic* or *geometric*. Then find the sum to the given term.

38. $13 + 15 + 17 + 19 + \ldots; S_{11}$ **39.** $8 + 20 + 50 + 125 + \ldots; S_7$

40. $3 + 15 + 75 + 375 + \ldots; S_7$ **41.** $4 + 9 + 14 + 19 + \ldots; S_8$

42. $6 + 12 + 24 + 48 + \ldots; S_7$ **43.** $13 + 6 + (-1) + (-8) + \ldots; S_{10}$

For each sum, find the number of terms, the first term, and the last term. Then evaluate the series.

44. $\sum_{n=1}^{5} (-8n + 4)$ **45.** $\sum_{n=1}^{7} 32\left(\frac{1}{4}\right)^{n-1}$

46. Open-Ended Write a sequence with a common difference of 7 and describe it using both an explicit and a recursive formula.

47. One section of a stadium has 50 rows. The front row has 30 seats with 2 more chairs in each successive row. The back row has 128 seats. Find the total number of seats in this section.

Given each set of axes, what does the area under the curve represent?

48. y-axis: pounds per inch^2; x-axis: inches^2

49. y-axis: meters per second; x-axis: seconds

50. y-axis: gallons per minute; x-axis: minutes

Graph each curve. Use inscribed rectangles 1 unit wide to approximate the area under the curve for the given interval.

51. $y = -x^2 + 6, -2 \le x \le 2$ **52.** $y = -\frac{1}{2}x + 6, 3 \le x \le 6$

Alternative Assessment

Form C

Chapter 11

Give complete answers and show all of your work.

TASK 1

    a. Use your graphing calculator to graph the function $f(x) = 2^x$ over the domain $\{x \mid x \geq 0\}$.

    b. Use the TABLE feature on your calculator to make a table of values of the function f for the set of x-values $1, 2, 3, \ldots$.

    c. Determine whether the sequence of function values is arithmetic, geometric, or neither. Justify your response.

    d. Write a recursive and an explicit formula for the sequence of function values.

    e. Find three terms of the sequence between 512 and 8192, and identify these as arithmetic or geometric means. Explain your reasoning.

TASK 2

    a. Determine whether the sequence $27, 9, 3, 1, \ldots$ is geometric, arithmetic, or neither. Justify your response.

    b. Write a recursive and an explicit formula for this sequence.

    c. Use summation notation to write the series related to the first ten terms of the sequence given in part a. Then evaluate this series.

    d. Use summation notation to write the series related to the infinite sequence given in part a. Determine whether this series diverges or converges. If the series converges, find its sum.

    e. Describe a real-world situation that could be modeled by the sequence given in part a.

Alternative Assessment (continued)   Form C

Chapter 11

TASK 3

a. Determine whether the sequence 2, 8, 14, 20, 26, . . . is arithmetic, geometric, or neither. Justify your response.

b. Write a recursive and an explicit formula for this sequence.

c. Find three terms of the sequence between 62 and 86, and identify these as arithmetic or geometric means. Explain your reasoning.

d. Use summation notation to write the series related to the infinite sequence given in part a. Find the sum of the first ten terms of the series.

e. Describe a real-world situation that can be modeled by the sequence given in part a.

TASK 4

a. Graph the function $f(x) = -0.5x^2 + 4.5$ for the domain $-3 \leq x \leq 3$ using your graphing calculator.

b. Carefully draw the graph of the function on a sheet of graph paper.

c. Draw and use inscribed rectangles 1 unit wide to approximate the area under the curve for the given interval.

d. Use $\int f(x)dx$ feature from the CALC menu of your graphing calculator to determine the area under the curve for the given interval.

Cumulative Review
Chapters 1–11

For Exercises 1–11, choose the correct letter.

1. Identify the conic section represented by the equation $\frac{x^2}{16} + \frac{y^2}{9} = 1$.
   A. circle
   B. ellipse
   C. parabola
   D. hyperbola

2. Which of these does not have the same value as the others?
   A. $\log_2 8$
   B. $\log_3 9$
   C. $\log_4 64$
   D. $\log_5 125$

3. Find $A + B$ if $A = \begin{bmatrix} 2 & 3 & -1 \\ 1 & 5 & 8 \end{bmatrix}$ and $B = \begin{bmatrix} 6 & 1 & -1 \\ -2 & 0 & 3 \end{bmatrix}$.

   A. $\begin{bmatrix} 8 & 4 & 0 \\ -1 & 5 & 11 \end{bmatrix}$
   B. $\begin{bmatrix} 8 & 4 & 2 \\ -1 & 5 & 11 \end{bmatrix}$
   C. $\begin{bmatrix} 8 & 2 & -2 \\ -1 & 5 & 11 \end{bmatrix}$
   D. $\begin{bmatrix} 8 & 4 & -2 \\ -1 & 5 & 11 \end{bmatrix}$

4. If $f(x) = 4x + 1$ and $g(x) = 2x^2$, what is the value of $g(f(-8))$?
   A. 1922
   B. 513
   C. 257
   D. −127

5. Which inequality is graphed?
   A. $y \leq x + 4$
   B. $y \leq x - 4$
   C. $y \geq x + 4$
   D. $y < x + 4$

6. Which expression represents the number of ways in which three cups from a group of five can be arranged on a shelf?
   A. $\frac{5!}{(5-3)!}$
   B. $\frac{5!}{3!}$
   C. $\frac{(5-3)!}{5!}$
   D. $\frac{5}{2}!$

7. Find the inverse of the function $y = 3x + 4$.
   A. $y = 3x - 4$
   B. $y = -\frac{1}{3}x + 4$
   C. $y = \frac{x-4}{3}$
   D. none of the above

8. A and B are two mutually exclusive events. $P(A) = \frac{1}{5}$ and $P(B) = \frac{3}{10}$. What is $P(A \text{ and } B)$?
   A. $\frac{1}{10}$
   B. $\frac{1}{2}$
   C. $\frac{3}{50}$
   D. $\frac{4}{15}$

9. The discriminant of a quadratic equation has a value of 0. Which of the following is true?
   A. There is one real solution.
   B. There is no real solution.
   C. There is one complex solution.
   D. There are two complex solutions.

Cumulative Review (continued)

Chapters 1–11

10. z varies directly with x and inversely with y. When $x = 5$ and $y = 2$, $z = 15$. Which of the following shows the correct relationship between x, y, and z?

A. $z = \frac{5x}{2}$ **B.** $z = \frac{6y}{x}$ **C.** $z = \frac{15x}{2y}$ **D.** $z = \frac{6x}{y}$

11. Which pair of numbers has a geometric mean of 12?

     A. 12 and 2   **B.** 24 and 6   **C.** 288 and 2   **D.** 14 and 10

Compare the quantity in Column A with that in Column B. Choose the best answer.

     A. The quantity in Column A is greater.

     B. The quantity in Column B is greater.

     C. The two quantities are equal.

     D. The relationship cannot be determined on the basis of the information supplied.

Column A	Column B
12. 0.99^{-1}	99^0
13. number of elements in a 7×4 matrix	number of elements in a 5×6 matrix

Find each answer.

14. Graph the system of inequalities $\begin{cases} y < 2x - 1 \\ y \geq -x + 3 \end{cases}$.

15. **Open-Ended** Write the equation of a parabola shifted the same number of units up and left.

16. **Writing** Explain how you can determine whether a sequence is *arithmetic* or *geometric*.

17. Multiply and simplify the expression.
$\sqrt[3]{12ab^2} \cdot \sqrt[3]{18a^5b}$

18. The population of a town was 30,000 in 2002, and it is growing by 2.3% each year. Write an equation to model the population of the town where t represents the number of years since 2002.

19. Solve $e^{x+5} = 16$.

20. Solve $\frac{1}{x} + 3 = \frac{5}{x}$. Check the solution.

21. Water leaks from a 10,000-gallon tank at a rate of 5 gallons per hour. Write a linear model for the situation and use it to find the amount of water in the tank after 24 hours.

Chapter 11 Answers

Practice 11-1

1. $a_n = a_{n-1} + 6$ where $a_1 = -14; 16$
2. $a_n = a_{n-1} - 0.3$ where $a_1 = 6; 4.5$
3. $a_n = -2a_{n-1}$ where $a_1 = 1; -32$
4. $a_n = 3a_{n-1}$ where $a_1 = 1; 81$
5. $a_n = \frac{1}{2}a_{n-1}$ where $a_1 = 1; \frac{1}{32}$
6. $a_n = a_{n-1} + \frac{1}{3}$ where $a_1 = \frac{2}{3}; 2\frac{1}{3}$
7. $a_n = a_{n-1} + 3$ where $a_1 = 36; 51$
8. $a_n = a_{n-1} - 6$ where $a_1 = 36; 6$
9. $a_n = \frac{1}{2}a_{n-1}$ where $a_1 = 9.6; 0.3$ **10.** $a_n = 7n; 140$
11. $a_n = 6n - 4; 116$ **12.** $a_n = n + 4; 24$
13. $a_n = n - 2; 18$ **14.** $a_n = 2n + 1; 41$
15. $a_n = 0.8n; 16$ **16.** $a_n = \frac{n}{4}; 5$ **17.** $a_n = \frac{1}{2n}; \frac{1}{40}$
18. $a_n = n - \frac{1}{3}; 19\frac{2}{3}$ **19.** multiply by 2; 32, 64, 128
20. subtract 5; 19, 14, 9 **21.** add 0.1; 1.2, 1.3, 1.4
22. add 7; 39, 46, 53 **23.** multiply by 2; 40, 80, 160
24. subtract 3; $-21, -24, -27$ **25.** explicit; $\frac{1}{3}, \frac{2}{3}, 1, \frac{4}{3}, \frac{5}{3}$
26. explicit; $-5, -2, 3, 10, 19$ **27.** recursive; 5, 8, 17, 44, 125
28. explicit; $0, \frac{1}{2}, 1, 1\frac{1}{2}, 2$ **29.** recursive; $5, -2, 5, -2, 5$
30. recursive; $-4, -8, -16, -32, -64$ **31a.** 1, 6, 36, 216
31b. $a_n = 6a_{n-1}$ where $a_1 = 1$ **32a.** $60°$ **32b.** $a_n = \frac{360}{n}$
32c. No polygon has one or two angles.

Practice 11-2

1. 96 **2.** -406.9 **3.** 36.3 **4.** -99 **5.** 464 **6.** -231 **7.** 5.5
8. -10.5 **9.** 171 **10.** no **11.** yes; -3 **12.** yes; -0.4
13. yes; 5 **14.** yes; -29 **15.** yes; 0.3 **16.** yes; 6 **17.** yes; 0.2
18. yes; 13 **19.** 36 **20.** 21 **21.** 31 **22.** 14.5 **23.** -42
24. -3.5 **25.** 0 **26.** -2 **27.** 21.5 **28.** -28.5 **29.** 227
30. 189.5 **31.** 4.5 **32.** 14.5 **33.** 9 **34.** $\frac{3}{5}$ **35.** -1 **36.** -6.5
37a. $a_n = a_{n-1} + 5$ where $a_1 = 32$ **37b.** 32, 37, 42, 47, 52
37c. $a_n = 32 + 5(n - 1)$ **37d.** 127 people

Practice 11-3

1. 8 **2.** 12 **3.** 4 **4.** 6 **5.** 10 **6.** 4.8 **7.** yes; 3; 243, 729
8. yes; 2; 64, 128 **9.** no **10.** yes; 2; 64, -128
11. yes; 0.5; 0.0625, 0.03125 **12.** yes; 0.3; 0.81, 0.243
13. no **14.** yes; -0.5; 4, -2 **15.** no
16. geometric; $\frac{1}{9}, \frac{1}{27}$ **17.** neither; $-9, -14$
18. geometric; 2, -2 **19.** arithmetic; 17, 22
20. arithmetic; $-11, -14$ **21.** neither; 5, -6
22. $a_n = 3(-2)^{n-1}; 3, -6, 12, -24, 48$
23. $a_n = 5(3)^{n-1}; 5, 15, 45, 135, 405$
24. $a_n = -1(4)^{n-1}; -1, -4, -16, -64, -256$
25. $a_n = -2(-3)^{n-1}; -2, 6, -18, 54, -162$

26. $a_n = 32(-0.5)^{n-1}; 32, -16, 8, -4, 2$
27. $a_n = 2187\left(\frac{1}{3}\right)^{n-1}; 2187, 729, 243, 81, 27$
28. $a_n = 9(2)^{n-1}; 9, 18, 36, 72, 144$
29. $a_n = -4(4)^{n-1}; -4, -16, -64, -256, -1024$
30. $a_n = 0.1(-2)^{n-1}; 0.1, -0.2, 0.4, -0.8, 1.6$
31a. about 19.2 in. **31b.** 9 mm **32a.** $a_n = 2537(1.025)^{n-1}$
32b. about 2732 **33a.** $a_n = 1(1.5)^{n-1}$ **33b.** 1.5 in.
33c. 2.25 in. **33d.** about 86.5 in.

Practice 11-4

1. 4; 0; 3; 6 **2.** 5; 3; 11; 35 **3.** 6; 28; 33; 183 **4.** 4; 13; 28; 82
5. 4; 2.5; 8.5; 22 **6.** 6; 2; -3; -3 **7.** 6; 5; 10; 45
8. 4; -4; -7; -22 **9.** 4; 11; 20; 62
10. $1 + 3 + 5 + 7 + 9 + 11 + 13 + 15; 64$
11. $5 + 8 + 11 + 14 + 17 + 20 + 23 + 26; 124$
12. $4 + 9 + 14 + 19 + 24 + 29 + 34 + 39 + 44; 216$
13. $10 + 25 + 40 + 55 + 70 + 85; 285$
14. $17 + 25 + 33 + 41 + 49 + 57 + 65; 287$
15. $125 + 126 + 127 + 128 + 129 + 130 + 131; 896$
16. $\sum_{n=1}^{7} (2n - 1)$ **17.** $\sum_{n=1}^{5} (0.3n + 2)$
18. $\sum_{n=1}^{4} 4n$ **19.** $\sum_{n=1}^{6} (-3n + 13)$
20. $\sum_{n=1}^{8} (4n - 1)$ **21.** $\sum_{n=1}^{7} (10n + 5)$
22. sequence; finite **23.** series; infinite **24.** sequence; infinite
25. series; finite **26.** sequence; infinite **27.** series; finite
28. -9 **29.** 39 **30.** -72 **31.** -51 **32.** 4.5 **33.** 60
34. 1025 stitches **35.** 19 musicians; 84 musicians

Practice 11-5

1. converges; yes **2.** converges; yes **3.** converges; yes
4. diverges; no **5.** converges; yes **6.** diverges; no **7.** 15
8. no sum **9.** $\frac{2}{3}$ **10.** no sum **11.** 16 **12.** 1.5 **13.** 600
14. 4000 **15.** arithmetic; 126 **16.** geometric; $\frac{255}{1024}$
17. geometric; 1023 **18.** arithmetic; 240 **19.** 79.921875
20. 28,697,812 **21.** about 74.99 **22.** 40.5 **23.** 0.22222222
24. 6300 **25.** $8553.71 **26.** $40,928.80 **27.** 5000 cm
28. about 177.78 mm **29.** $2,319,367.05; $4,950,000

Practice 11-6

For Exercises 1–19, answers are in units^2.
1a. $0.5(3.75) + 0.5(3) + 0.5(1.75) + 0.5(0); 4.25$
1b. $0.5(4) + 0.5(3.75) + 0.5(3) + 0.5(1.75); 6.25$
2a. $0.5(15.5) + 0.5(14) + 0.5(11.5) + 0.5(8); 24.5$
2b. $0.5(16) + 0.5(15.5) + 0.5(14) + 0.5(11.5); 28.5$
3a. $0.5(1.875) + 0.5(1.5) + 0.5(0.875) + 0.5(0); 2.125$
3b. $0.5(2) + 0.5(1.875) + 0.5(1.5) + 0.5(0.875); 3.125$
4a. $0.5(4) + 0.5(4.25) + 0.5(5) + 0.5(6.25); 9.75$
4b. $0.5(4.25) + 0.5(5) + 0.5(6.25) + 0.5(8); 11.75$

5a. $0.5(6) + 0.5(6.5) + 0.5(8) + 0.5(10.5); 15.5$
5b. $0.5(6.5) + 0.5(8) + 0.5(10.5) + 0.5(14); 19.5$
6a. $0.5(2) + 0.5(2.125) + 0.5(2.5) + 0.5(3.125); 4.875$
6b. $0.5(2.125) + 0.5(2.5) + 0.5(3.125) + 0.5(4); 5.875$
7a. $0.5(14.25) + 0.5(12) + 0.5(8.25) + 0.5(3); 18.75$
7b. $0.5(15) + 0.5(14.25) + 0.5(12) + 0.5(8.25); 24.75$
8a. $0.5(2) + 0.5(2.75) + 0.5(5) + 0.5(8.75); 9.25$
8b. $0.5(2.75) + 0.5(5) + 0.5(8.75) + 0.5(14); 15.25$
9a. $0.5(9.75) + 0.5(9) + 0.5(7.75) + 0.5(6); 16.25$
9b. $0.5(10) + 0.5(9.75) + 0.5(9) + 0.5(7.75); 18.25$
10a.

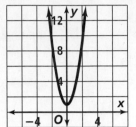

10b. 5.5 **10c.** 9.5 **10d.** 7.5; the mean
11. 6.75 **12.** 16.5 **13.** 9 **14.** 12 **15.** 2.25 **16.** 18 **17.** 9
18. 6 **19.** $4.\overline{6}$ **20.** total feet **21.** total number of computers
22. total miles **23.** total gallons **24.** total molecules
25. total price
26.

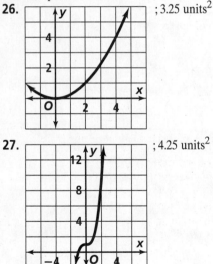

; 3.25 units^2

27.

; 4.25 units^2

Reteaching 11-1

1. subtract 5; 18, 13, 8 **2.** multiply by 2; 112, 224, 448
3. subtract 2; $-13, -15, -17$ **4.** multiply by 3; 162, 486, 1458
5. add 0.5; 6.5, 7, 7.5 **6.** each time the addend increases by 2;
37, 47, 59 **7.** B **8.** E **9.** A **10.** F **11.** C **12.** D

Reteaching 11-2

1. -28 **2.** 0.0129 **3.** -92 **4.** 12.2 **5.** 18.8 **6.** 118
7. \$110 **8.** \$143 **9.** 31 rows

Reteaching 11-3

1. $\frac{1}{128}$ **2.** $\frac{10,935}{128}$ **3.** $-\frac{2}{59,049}$ **4.** $\frac{64}{729}$ **5.** 25,600 **6.** 512

7. $a_n = 1\left(\frac{1}{2}\right)^{n-1}; 1, \frac{1}{2}, \frac{1}{4}, \frac{1}{8}, \frac{1}{16}$

8. $a_n = 2(3)^{n-1}; 2, 6, 18, 54, 162$

9. $a_n = 12(3)^{n-1}; 12, 36, 108, 324, 972$

10. $a_n = 1\left(\frac{1}{4}\right)^{n-1}; 1, \frac{1}{4}, \frac{1}{16}, \frac{1}{64}, \frac{1}{256}$

11. $a_n = 5\left(\frac{1}{10}\right)^{n-1}; 5, \frac{1}{2}, \frac{1}{20}, \frac{1}{200}, \frac{1}{2000}$

12. $a_n = 1\left(\frac{1}{3}\right)^{n-1}; 1, \frac{1}{3}, \frac{1}{9}, \frac{1}{27}, \frac{1}{81}$

13. $a_n = 5(2)^{n-1}; 5, 10, 20, 40, 80$
14. $a_n = 1(3)^{n-1}; 1, 3, 9, 27, 81$
15. $a_n = 3(6)^{n-1}; 3, 18, 108, 648, 3888$
16. $a_n = 3(3)^{n-1}; 3, 9, 27, 81, 243$
17. $a_n = 2(2)^{n-1}; 2, 4, 8, 16, 32$

18. $a_n = 2\left(\frac{1}{2}\right)^{n-1}; 2, 1, \frac{1}{2}, \frac{1}{4}, \frac{1}{8}$

19. $a_n = 1\left(\frac{1}{5}\right)^{n-1}; 1, \frac{1}{5}, \frac{1}{25}, \frac{1}{125}, \frac{1}{625}$

20. $a_n = 3(4)^{n-1}; 3, 12, 48, 192, 768$

21. $a_n = 5\left(\frac{1}{4}\right)^{n-1}; 5, \frac{5}{4}, \frac{5}{16}, \frac{5}{64}, \frac{5}{256}$

Reteaching 11-4

1. -6 **2.** $\frac{25}{36}$ **3.** 93 **4.** 22 **5.** -56
6. 120 **7.** 108 **8.** -35 **9.** 74
10. $a_n = 87 + 2n; 5985$ seats

Reteaching 11-5

1. 4095 **2.** $\frac{341}{32}$ **3.** $-\frac{635}{32}$ **4.** $\frac{3415}{512}$ **5.** 20 **6.** $-\frac{11}{13}$ **7.** 2
8. $\frac{5}{14}$ **9.** $-\frac{1}{9}$ **10.** 100 **11.** 18 **12.** $\frac{1}{6}$ **13.** $\frac{5}{6}$

Reteaching 11-6

Answers are in units^2.
1. 3.5 **2.** 4.25 **3.** 9 **4.** 1.5 **5.** 3.75 **6.** 8.25

Enrichment 11-1

6; 12; 16; 14; 11; 2; 4; 15; 5; 3; 13; 7; 10; 1; 17; 9
SIMILAR TRIANGLES

Chapter 11 Answers (continued)

Enrichment 11-2

a_1	d	a_1	d
-1	-1	1	-2
2	-1	2	4
-2	4	1	4
1	1	-3	4
-2	-2	-1	-4
0	0	0	-3
-1	4	-3	-3
0	4		

	C1	C2	C3	C4	C5	C6	C7	C8	C9	C10
R1		W							S	
R2			H						A	
R3	T			A					L	
R4		U			L				M	
R5			N			E			O	
R6			A						N	

tuna, whale, salmon

Enrichment 11-3

1. Each term is $1\frac{1}{2}$ times the preceding term.　**2.** 2; 2 terms
3. 3, 3.3, 3.63, 3.99, 4.39, 4.83, 5.31, 5.85, 6.43, 7.07
4. 8 terms;　8 terms; $1 < |r| < 2$　**5.** 7; $\sqrt{2}$; 2 terms
6. 10; $\sqrt[3]{2}$; 3 terms　**7.** 2

Enrichment 11-4

1. $2S$　**2.** 101　**3.** 100　**4.** $100 \times 101 = 10,100$
5. $2S = 10,100$; $S = 5050$　**6.** $a_1 + (n-1)d$
7. $S = a_1 + (a_1 + d) + \ldots + [a_1 + (n-1)d]$;
$\quad S = [a_1 + (n-1)d] + \ldots + (a_1 + d) + a_1$
8. $2a_1 + (n-1)d$　**9.** n　**10.** $n[2a_1 + (n-1)d]$

11. $2S = n[2a_1 + (n-1)d]$; $S = \dfrac{n[2a_1 + (n-1)d]}{2}$

12.
$$S = \frac{n[2a_1 + (n-1)d]}{2}$$
$$= \frac{n[a_1 + a_1 + (n-1)d]}{2}$$
$$= \frac{n[a_1 + [a_1 + (n-1)d]]}{2}$$
$$= \frac{n[a_1 + u_n]}{2}$$
$$= \frac{n}{2}(a_1 + a_n)$$

Enrichment 11-5

1.

4	8	15
5	16	31
6	32	63

2. 1　**3.** geometric; common ratio: 2

4. $a_{n+1} = 2a_n$ where $a_1 = 1$　**5.** $a_{n+1} - 1(2)^n$
6. 16,384; the number of grains of wheat on square 15
7. neither　**8.** S_n is less than a_{n+1}.
9. $S_n = 2a_n - 1$ where $a_1 = 1$　**10.** $S_n = 2^n - 1$
11. 536,870,911; the total number of grains of wheat on
squares 1 through 29, inclusive　**12.** 2^{n-1} matches
13. 2^{n-1} losers; 2^{n-1} winners　**14.** 2^{n-2} matches
15. 2^{n-2} losers; 2^{n-2} winners

Enrichment 11-6

1. 1,696,188 L　**2.** the second hour; 625,000 L　**3.** 2,520,000 L;
During the first and second hours, the volume of water was the
same; 900,000 L　**4.** 70 L/s

Chapter Project

Activity 1: Researching
• Check students' work.
• Check students' work; Answers may vary. Sample: The
lengths form an arithmetic sequence; Answers may vary.
Sample: The lines of sight along the tops and bottoms of the
arrows meet at a vanishing point.
• Check students' work; Answers may vary. Sample: There is
no longer a vanishing point.
• Check students' work.

Activity 2: Creating
Check students' work.

Activity 3: Analyzing
Check students' work.

✔ Checkpoint Quiz 1

1. arithmetic; 6　**2.** geometric; 1.5　**3.** arithmetic; 10
4. geometric; 4　**5.** arithmetic; -2　**6.** geometric; 0.75
7. 5　**8.** 35　**9.** 8　**10.** If the common ratio is greater than 1,
the terms increase. If the common ratio is between 0 and 1,
the terms decrease. If the common ratio is 1, the terms neither
increase nor decrease. (Note: If the common ratio is less
than 1, the sequence no longer has only positive terms.)
11. $a_n = a_{n+1} + 2$; $392

✔ Checkpoint Quiz 2

1. geometric; 3280　**2.** arithmetic; 96　**3.** arithmetic; 762
4. geometric; $\dfrac{14,197}{16}$　**5.** geometric; $-14,762$
6. arithmetic; 175　**7.** $\dfrac{2}{3}$　**8.** 5　**9.** Answers may vary.
Sample: $1.2 + 0.2 - 0.8 - \ldots - 8.8 = -41.8$　**10.** Answers
may vary. Sample: No, the terms of the series grow in absolute
value so they cannot have a finite sum; Two possible series
with $r = 2$ are $3 + 6 + 12 + 24 + \ldots$ and $(-1) + (-2)$
$+ (-4) + \ldots$.

Chapter 11 Answers (continued)

Chapter Test, Form A

1. $a_n = a_{n-1} + 5$ where $a_1 = 41$; $a_n = 41 + 5(n-1)$ or $a_n = 36 + 5n$; 86

2. $a_n = 10a_{n-1}$ where $a_1 = 1$; $a_n = 1(10)^{n-1}$; 1,000,000,000

3. $a_n = 2a_{n-1}$ where $a_1 = 3$; $a_n = 3(2)^{n-1}$; 1536

4a. $a_n = 20 + 3(n-1)$ **4b.** $a_n = a_{n-1} + 3$ where $a_1 = 20$

4c. 62 bulbs **4d.** 615 bulbs **5.** geometric; 196,608

6. arithmetic; -42 **7.** geometric; $\frac{2}{78,125}$ **8.** arithmetic; $\frac{25}{2}$

9. 13 **10.** 2 **11.** $\frac{5}{2}$ **12.** $\frac{7}{3}$

13. Answers may vary. Sample: 30, 300, 3000, 30,000, 300,000, ...; $a_n = 10a_{n-1}$ where $a_1 = 30$; $a_n = 30(10)^{n-1}$

14. arithmetic; -66, **15.** geometric; 2.5 **16.** geometric; -4

17. arithmetic; 17 **18.** geometric; $\frac{1}{3}$ **19.** arithmetic; $\frac{1}{3}$

20. 3, -6, 12, -24 **21.** 6, 10, 14, 18 **22.** 1000, 100, 10, 1

23. $-4, -6, -8, -10$ **24.** $\frac{1}{2}, -\frac{3}{2}, \frac{9}{2}, -\frac{27}{2}$

25. $-100, -10, -1, -\frac{1}{10}$ **26.** 8 **27.** 75 **28.** 10 **29.** 7

30. $\frac{3}{2}$ **31.** 12 **32.** 120 **33.** 12.5 **34.** 24 **35.** $\frac{8}{3}$ **36.** $-8\frac{1}{10}$

37. -10 **38.** arithmetic; 230 **39.** geometric; 4445

40. geometric; -9840 **41.** arithmetic; 93 **42.** arithmetic; 10

43. geometric; $\frac{15,624}{625}$ **44.** 6; 3; -7; -12

45. 5; 4; 0.25; 7.75 **46.** Answers may vary. Sample:

$$\sum_{n=1}^{\infty} 5(1)^{n-1} = 5 + 5 + 5 + \ldots; \text{ The series diverges}$$

because the number 5 is added an infinite number of times.

47. 330 blocks **48.** feet per second **49.** total dollars

50. total calories

51. 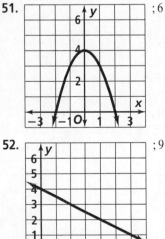 ; 6

52. ; 9

Chapter Test, Form B

1. $a_n = a_{n-1} + 7$ where $a_1 = 23$; $a_n = 23 + 7(n-1)$ or $a_n = 16 + 7n$; 86

2. $a_n = 4a_{n-1}$ where $a_1 = \frac{1}{16}$; $a_n = \frac{1}{16}(4)^{n-1}$; 16,384

3. $a_n = a_{n-1} + 2$ where $a_1 = 5$; $a_n = 5 + 2(n-1)$ or $a_n = 3 + 2n$; 23

4a. $a_n = 1 + 0.25(n-1)$

4b. $a_n = a_{n-1} + 0.25$ where $a_1 = 1$ **4c.** 4.5 in.

4d. 41.25 in. **5.** neither; 47 **6.** geometric; $\frac{1}{64}$

7. geometric; $\frac{1}{32}$ **8.** geometric; $\frac{1}{4374}$ **9.** 31 **10.** -14

11. 2 **12.** $-\frac{31}{5}$ **13.** Find the product of the two numbers then take the square root of that product. **14.** geometric; 2.5

15. arithmetic; -54 **16.** arithmetic; 32 **17.** geometric; -6

18. arithmetic; $-\frac{2}{3}$ **19.** geometric; $\frac{1}{4}$ **20.** 4, -8, 16, -32

21. 22, 26, 30, 34 **22.** 100, 10, 1, $\frac{1}{10}$ **23.** 3, -6, 12, -24

24. $\frac{1}{6}, \frac{5}{3}, \frac{19}{6}, \frac{14}{3}$ **25.** $-12, 2, -\frac{1}{3}, \frac{1}{18}$ **26.** 100 **27.** 36

28. 30 **29.** $\frac{3}{2}$ **30.** 6 **31.** 6 **32.** $\frac{100}{9}$ **33.** $\frac{27}{4}$ **34.** $\frac{45}{2}$

35. 4 **36.** $\frac{16}{3}$ **37.** $-\frac{64}{3}$ **38.** arithmetic; 253

39. geometric; 3249.875 **40.** geometric; 58,593

41. arithmetic; 172 **42.** geometric; 762 **43.** arithmetic; -185

44. 5; -4; -36; -100 **45.** 7; 32; $\frac{1}{128}$; $\frac{5461}{128}$

46. Answers may vary. Sample: 1, 8, 15, 22, 29, ...; $a_n = 7 + a_{n-1}$ where $a_1 = 1$; $a_n = 1 + 7(n-1)$

47. 3950 seats **48.** total pounds **49.** total meters

50. total gallons

51. ; 14

52. 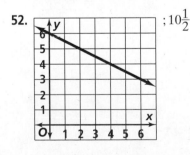 ; $10\frac{1}{2}$

Alternative Assessment, Form C

TASK 1 Scoring Guide:

a.

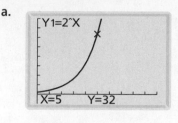

b.

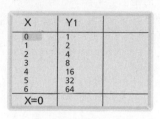

c. geometric; There is a common ratio of 2.

d. $a_n = 2a_{n-1}$ where $a_1 = 2$; $a_n = 2^n$

e. 1024, 2048, and 4096; geometric means; 2048 is the square root of the product of 512 and 8192, 1024 is the square root of the product of 512 and 2048, and 4096 is the square root of the product of 2048 and 8192.

3 Student correctly uses graphing calculator to view the function and to construct a table of values using positive integers for x-values. Student correctly writes formulas for the sequence and determines that the sequence is geometric with an appropriate justification. Student correctly finds the three missing geometric means.

2 Student correctly uses graphing calculator to view the function and to construct a table of values with only minor errors. Student writes formulas for the sequence with only minor errors. Student determines that the sequence is geometric and provides a justification. Student finds the three missing geometric means with only minor errors.

1 Student determines a minimal amount of information about this sequence, its formulas, and the geometric means. There are major errors in logic.

0 Student makes no attempt, or no response is given.

TASK 2 Scoring Guide:

a. geometric; There is a common ratio of $\frac{1}{3}$.

b. $a_n = \frac{1}{3}a_{n-1}$ where $a_1 = 27$; $a_n = 27\left(\frac{1}{3}\right)^{n-1}$

c. $\sum_{n=1}^{10} 27\left(\frac{1}{3}\right)^{n-1}$; $\frac{29,524}{729}$

d. $\sum_{n=1}^{\infty} 27\left(\frac{1}{3}\right)^{n-1}$; converges; $\frac{81}{2}$

e. Check students' work.

3 Student correctly determines that the sequence is geometric. Student correctly finds the formulas for the sequence and the series. Student correctly finds the sum of the first ten terms of the series, determines that the series converges, and correctly determines the sum. Student describes a feasible real-world situation for this sequence.

2 Student correctly determines that the sequence is geometric. Student finds the formulas for the sequence and the series with only minor errors. Student finds the sum of the first ten terms of the series with only minor errors. Student determines that the series converges and determines the sum with only minor errors. Student describes a real-world situation for this sequence.

1 Student determines a minimal amount of information about this sequence and its related series. There are major errors in logic. The real-world example is inappropriate or missing.

0 Student makes no attempt, or no response is given.

TASK 3 Scoring Guide:

a. arithmetic; There is a common difference of 6.

b. $a_n = 6 + a_{n-1}$ where $a_1 = 2$; $a_n = 2 + 6(n - 1)$

c. 68, 74, and 80; arithmetic means; 74 is the average of 62 and 86, 68 is the average of 62 and 74, and 80 is the average of 74 and 86.

d. $\sum_{n=1}^{\infty} (6n - 4)$; 290   e. Check students' work.

3 Student correctly determines that the sequence is arithmetic and provides a reasonable justification. Student correctly finds the three means and identifies them as arithmetic. Student correctly finds the formula for the series. Student correctly finds the sum of the first ten terms of the series. Student describes a feasible real-world situation for this sequence.

2 Student correctly determines that the sequence is arithmetic and provides a justification. Student finds the three means with minor errors, and identifies them as arithmetic. Student finds the formula for the series with only minor errors. Student finds the sum of the first ten terms of the series with only minor errors. Student describes a real-world situation for this sequence.

1 Student determines a minimal amount of information about this sequence, its formulas, and the arithmetic means. Student neglects to describe a real-world situation. There are major errors in logic.

0 Student makes no attempt, or no response is given.

TASK 4 Scoring Guide:

a.

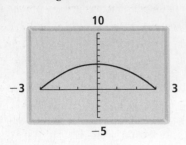

b. Check students' drawing.

c. 13 units^2

d. 18 units^2

3 Student correctly graphs the function over the designated domain on a graphing calculator. Student draws a neat graph of the function on graph paper. Student makes a close estimate of the area under the curve using rectangles. Student correctly uses a graphing calculator to find the area under the curve.

2 Student graphs the function on a graphing calculator. Student draws a graph of the function on graph paper. Student makes an estimate of the area under the curve using rectangles. Student uses a graphing calculator to find the area under the curve with only minor errors.

1 Student does not graph the function correctly using a graphing calculator. The graph on graph paper contains major errors. There are major errors in the calculation of the area under the curve using rectangles. Student does not use a graphing calculator to find the area under the curve.

0 Student makes no attempt, or no response is given.

Cumulative Review

1. B **2.** B **3.** D **4.** A **5.** A **6.** A **7.** C **8.** C **9.** A
10. D **11.** B **12.** A **13.** B
14.

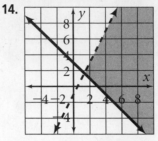

15. Answers may vary. Sample: $y = 2(x + 3)^2 + 3$
16. An arithmetic sequence has a common difference between two successive terms, while a geometric sequence has a common ratio between two successive terms. **17.** $6a^2b$
18. $P = 30,000(1.023)^t$ **19.** $-5 + \ln 16 \approx -2.23$
20. $\frac{4}{3}$ **21.** $W = -5t + 10,000$; 9880 gal